# THIS PLANNER

## Belongs To:

_____

# ALL ABOUT

## 1. What are you most grateful for in your life?

Keeping track of what you're most grateful for will keep you focused on the blessings in your life. Consider the many reasons you have to be grateful BELOW:

## 2. What do you love about yourself?

Self love isn't always easy but writing down what you're most proud of will help clear your mind of the criticism and negativity you may feel.

## 3. Where is your happy place?

Where do you feel most at peace? Do you have a favorite spot that allows you to refocus your energy, find inner peace and feel happiness? Describe your happy place.

# ALL ABOUT *me*

### 4. What do you enjoy doing?

What are your favorite activities where you are able to boost your mood and free your mind? This could be a hobby or physical activity, or perhaps something entirely different.

### 5. Who can you rely on?

Describe the people in your life that you can count on when things get tough.  Who do you feel closest to?

### 6. How can you improve your life?

What changes can you make that will ultimately improve your life and give you joy? This could be career or personal related. Please share your thoughts below.

# ALL ABOUT *me*

### 7. My greatest accomplishments are:

What are some of the things you are most proud of?

### 8. What do you wish others knew about you?

What do you wish others knew about who you really are? What do you feel others overlook?

### 9. What are your greatest aspirations?

Whether it be personal, career or family goals, list them below.

# DEAR FUTURE *Self...*

FAMILY GOALS

CAREER GOALS

SELF CARE

RELATIONSHIP

HEALTH GOALS

FRIENDSHIPS

PERSONAL

FINANCIAL

TRAVEL

PASSIONS

NEW SKILLS

OTHER

5 YEARS FROM NOW

10 YEARS FROM NOW

# COPING *Strategies*

**Write down the different ways you feel about yourself as well as personal situations, and how you can better manage and cope with self-doubt and negative feelings.**

| WHEN I'M FEELING... | I WILL MANAGE IT BY... |
|---|---|
| | |
| WHEN I'M FEELING... | I WILL MANAGE IT BY... |
| | |
| WHEN I'M FEELING... | I WILL MANAGE IT BY... |
| | |
| WHEN I'M FEELING... | I WILL MANAGE IT BY... |
| | |
| WHEN I'M FEELING... | I WILL MANAGE IT BY... |
| | |
| WHEN I'M FEELING... | I WILL MANAGE IT BY... |
| | |
| WHEN I'M FEELING... | I WILL MANAGE IT BY... |
| | |

OTHER IDEAS / NOTES

# ANXIETY *debrief*

**Describe a situation where you felt anxious:**

**What were the physical symptoms you experienced?**

**Did you face the situation or remove yourself from it?**

**How did you cope with this anxiety? Do you believe your thoughts and reactions were rational?**

# ANXIETY *levels*

**Use the chart below to rate your level of anxiety when facing various situations by coloring the boxes:**

**SITUATION:** Meeting Someone New

**ANXIETY LEVEL**

**DO YOU:** Face this fear | Avoid this situation

**SITUATION:** Going to the grocery store

**ANXIETY LEVEL**

**DO YOU:** Face this fear | Avoid this situation

**SITUATION:** Stating your opinion when potentially controversial or opposing.

**ANXIETY LEVEL**

**DO YOU:** Face this fear | Avoid this situation

**SITUATION:** Stand up for yourself when treated unfairly or poorly.

**ANXIETY LEVEL**

**DO YOU:** Face this fear | Avoid this situation

**SITUATION:** Spending time alone with friends and/or family.

**ANXIETY LEVEL**

**DO YOU:** Face this fear | Avoid this situation

**SITUATION:** Being watched/observed when doing something/completing a task or activity.

**ANXIETY LEVEL**

**DO YOU:** Face this fear | Avoid this situation

# UNDERSTANDING *anxiety*

**Understanding the origin of your anxiety will help you learn new ways to manage your responses.**

| SITUATION: | Meeting Someone New | WHAT IS YOUR BIGGEST FEAR WHEN FACING THIS SITUATION? |
|---|---|---|

| SITUATION: | Going to the grocery store | WHAT IS YOUR BIGGEST FEAR WHEN FACING THIS SITUATION? |
|---|---|---|

| SITUATION: | Stating your opinion. | WHAT IS YOUR BIGGEST FEAR WHEN FACING THIS SITUATION? |
|---|---|---|

| SITUATION: | Stand up for yourself. | WHAT IS YOUR BIGGEST FEAR WHEN FACING THIS SITUATION? |
|---|---|---|

| SITUATION: | Spending time alone with friends. | WHAT IS YOUR BIGGEST FEAR WHEN FACING THIS SITUATION? |
|---|---|---|

| SITUATION: | Being watched/observed. | WHAT IS YOUR BIGGEST FEAR WHEN FACING THIS SITUATION? |
|---|---|---|

# GRATEFUL *Life*

What are the things you are most grateful for? Spend time self-reflecting on the many blessings in your life. Shift your focus on gratitude and rid yourself of negative emotions and toxic thoughts.

| 1 | 2 | 3 |
|---|---|---|
| 4 | 5 | 6 |
| 7 | 8 | 9 |
| 10 | 11 | 12 |

# HAPPINESS Is...

**Complete the following sentences to refocus your mind on the joys in your life:**

## I FEEL MOST RELAXED WHEN:

## I AM LESS STRESSED WHEN:

## MY STRENGTHS ARE:

## I AM A GOOD FRIEND BECAUSE:

## I AM MOST EXCITED BY:

## I AM MOST FOCUSED WHEN:

## I FEEL MOST APPRECIATED WHEN:

## I AM MOST MOTIVATED WHEN:

# THOUGHTS *Tracker*

MONITORING YOUR THOUGHTS & FEELINGS

MONDAY'S THOUGHTS

TUESDAY'S THOUGHTS

WEDNESDAY'S THOUGHTS

THURSDAY'S THOUGHTS

FRIDAY'S THOUGHTS

SATURDAY'S THOUGHTS

SUNDAY'S THOUGHTS

# TRANSFORMING *Thoughts*

TRANSFORMING NEGATIVE THOUGHTS

**We all deal with negative thoughts and self-doubt. Use this space to keep track of those feelings and focus on how you can replace them with positive thoughts that promote self-growth.**

| NEGATIVE THOUGHT | REPLACEMENT THOUGHT |
|---|---|
| | |
| NEGATIVE THOUGHT | REPLACEMENT THOUGHT |
| | |
| NEGATIVE THOUGHT | REPLACEMENT THOUGHT |
| | |
| NEGATIVE THOUGHT | REPLACEMENT THOUGHT |
| | |
| NEGATIVE THOUGHT | REPLACEMENT THOUGHT |
| | |
| NEGATIVE THOUGHT | REPLACEMENT THOUGHT |
| | |

PERSONAL REFLECTIONS

# SELF AWARENESS *Chart*

It's easy to get lost in our own headspace so it's important that you question any negative feelings so you can sort through your emotions effectively. Use this worksheet to document your progress.

THOUGHT

IS THE THOUGHT VALID?

HOW DO YOU REACT TO THIS NEGATIVE THOUGHT?

WHAT COULD YOU DO TO AVOID FEELING THIS WAY?

THOUGHTS & REFLECTIONS

# MOOD Chart

Use the wheel below to document your moods every month.
Use 3 different colors to represent positive, negative or neutral emotions.

POSITIVE    NEGATIVE    NEUTRAL

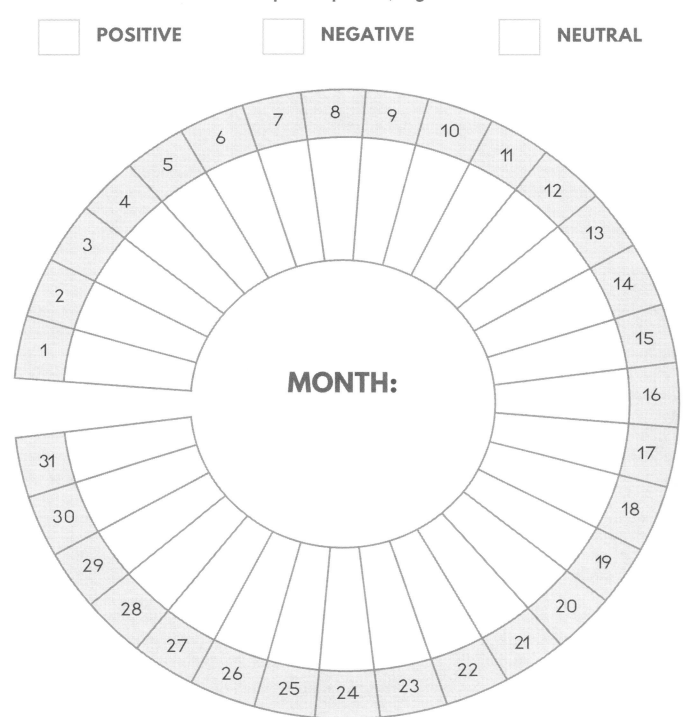

MONTH:

# SLEEP Tracker

MONTH:

Sleep plays a major factor in our ability to cope with anxiety and depression. Keep track of your sleep pattern in order to determine how the amount of rest may be affecting your mental health.

| DAY | HOURS SLEPT | QUALITY OF SLEEP | THOUGHTS |
|---|---|---|---|
| 1 | | | |
| 2 | | | |
| 3 | | | |
| 4 | | | |
| 5 | | | |
| 6 | | | |
| 7 | | | |
| 8 | | | |
| 9 | | | |
| 10 | | | |
| 11 | | | |
| 12 | | | |
| 13 | | | |
| 14 | | | |
| 15 | | | |
| 16 | | | |
| 17 | | | |
| 18 | | | |
| 19 | | | |
| 20 | | | |
| 21 | | | |
| 22 | | | |
| 23 | | | |
| 24 | | | |
| 25 | | | |
| 26 | | | |
| 27 | | | |
| 28 | | | |
| 29 | | | |
| 30 | | | |
| 31 | | | |

# LIFE *Assessment*

## TOP 3 AREAS OF YOUR LIFE YOU'D LIKE TO **IMPROVE**

01

02

03

## 3 WAYS YOU CAN **ACCOMPLISH** YOUR LIFE GOALS

# TRIGGER *Tracker*

**Keep track of experiences that generate negative thoughts and emotions.**

| DATE | INCIDENT | REACTION |
|------|----------|----------|
|      |          |          |
|      |          |          |
|      |          |          |
|      |          |          |
|      |          |          |
|      |          |          |
|      |          |          |
|      |          |          |
|      |          |          |
|      |          |          |
|      |          |          |
|      |          |          |
|      |          |          |
|      |          |          |

# GRATEFUL *Heart*

DAY | TODAY I AM GRATEFUL FOR:

1

2

3

4

5

6

7

8

9

10

11

12

13

14

15

16

17

18

19

20

21

22

23

24

25

26

27

28

29

30

31

# SELF Improvement

## WHAT ARE YOUR SELF SABOTAGE HABITS?

**Eliminate Negative Habits**

**Create Positive Habits**

## HOW CAN YOU IMPROVE YOUR MENTAL HEALTH?

**What Key Areas Need Work?**

**What Are Some Steps You Can Take?**

## ANALYZING THE PEOPLE IN YOUR LIFE

**Who Are The Negative Influences?**

**Who Are The Positive Influences?**

## HOW DO I HOLD MYSELF ACCOUNTABLE?

**What I Know I'm Responsible For**

**Who Helps Keep Me Accountable?**

# SELF CARE *Ideas*

## NURTURE YOUR MIND

Discover new hobbies
Read a book
Take a road trip
Keep a journal
Talk to a friend

Follow inspiring people
Challenge yourself
Be grateful
Call an old friend
Try something new

## FEED YOUR SPIRIT

Have "me-time"
Listen to music
Read poetry
Write "future-self"
Paint
Meditate

## TAKE CARE OF YOUR BODY

Eat healthy
Start a workout plan
Get enough sleep
Stay hydrated
Yoga

*Ideas*

# SELF CARE *Planner*

**Self-care involves taking care of yourself emotionally, mentally and physically.
Create a self-care plan by adding activities to the categories below.**

MENTAL SELF-CARE

PHYSICAL SELF-CARE (GET ACTIVE)

EMOTIONAL SELF-CARE

DAILY HABITS (SLEEP, ETC.)

REACH OUT (SOCIALIZE)

SUPPORT NETWORK

OTHER:

# SELF CARE *Tracker*

Self care is an important step in managing anxiety and depression. It helps us recharge, reset and nurtures our mind and soul.  Focus on incorporating one self-care activity into your daily life.

# THOUGHT *Log*

**Keep track of negative thoughts so you can learn how to control irrational responses and triggers.**

| DATE | INCIDENT | INITIAL REACTION | RATIONAL REACTION |
|------|----------|------------------|-------------------|
|      |          |                  |                   |
|      |          |                  |                   |
|      |          |                  |                   |
|      |          |                  |                   |
|      |          |                  |                   |
|      |          |                  |                   |
|      |          |                  |                   |
|      |          |                  |                   |
|      |          |                  |                   |
|      |          |                  |                   |
|      |          |                  |                   |
|      |          |                  |                   |
|      |          |                  |                   |
|      |          |                  |                   |
|      |          |                  |                   |
|      |          |                  |                   |

# PERSONAL Wins

MONTH:

It's important to celebrate both minor and major wins when it comes to your mental health and the coping strategies you've learned along the way.  You've come a long way!

## 2 RECENT WINS

|  |  |
|--|--|
|  |  |

## TOP 3 MILESTONES

| 1 |
|---|
| 2 |
| 3 |

## 3 THINGS I'VE LEARNED ABOUT MYSELF OVER THE LAST YEAR

|  |  |  |
|--|--|--|
|  |  |  |

| PERSONAL REFLECTIONS | HOW I'VE LEARNED TO COPE WITH EMOTIONS |
|----------------------|----------------------------------------|
|  |  |
|  |  |
|  |  |
|  |  |
|  |  |

## NOTES

|  |
|--|
|  |
|  |
|  |
|  |
|  |
|  |

# PERSONAL *Rewards*

MONTH:

Make sure to reward yourself for accomplishments throughout your journey.
Whether it's a visit to your favorite restaurant, a bubble bath or an evening with friends, it's
important to celebrate your progress every step of the way.

## IDEAS FOR PERSONAL REWARDS

| 1 | 2 |
|---|---|
| 3 | 4 |
| 5 | 6 |

| HOW I FELT BEFORE | HOW I REWARDED MYSELF | HOW I FELT AFTER REWARD |
|---|---|---|
| | | |
| | | |
| | | |
| | | |
| | | |
| | | |

| NOTES | PERSONAL REFLECTIONS/THOUGHTS |
|---|---|
| | |

# ANXIETY *Tracker*

Document the days when you experienced anxiety. This page includes a 3-week tracker.

**ANXIETY LEVELS (1-MILD, 10 SEVERE)**

| | | | | | | | | | | | | |
|---|---|---|---|---|---|---|---|---|---|---|---|---|
| MON | 01 | 02 | 03 | 04 | 05 | 06 | 07 | 08 | 09 | 10 | 11 | 12 |
| TUE | 01 | 02 | 03 | 04 | 05 | 06 | 07 | 08 | 09 | 10 | 11 | 12 |
| WED | 01 | 02 | 03 | 04 | 05 | 06 | 07 | 08 | 09 | 10 | 11 | 12 |
| THU | 01 | 02 | 03 | 04 | 05 | 06 | 07 | 08 | 09 | 10 | 11 | 12 |
| FRI | 01 | 02 | 03 | 04 | 05 | 06 | 07 | 08 | 09 | 10 | 11 | 12 |
| SAT | 01 | 02 | 03 | 04 | 05 | 06 | 07 | 08 | 09 | 10 | 11 | 12 |
| SUN | 01 | 02 | 03 | 04 | 05 | 06 | 07 | 08 | 09 | 10 | 11 | 12 |
| MON | 01 | 02 | 03 | 04 | 05 | 06 | 07 | 08 | 09 | 10 | 11 | 12 |
| TUE | 01 | 02 | 03 | 04 | 05 | 06 | 07 | 08 | 09 | 10 | 11 | 12 |
| WED | 01 | 02 | 03 | 04 | 05 | 06 | 07 | 08 | 09 | 10 | 11 | 12 |
| THU | 01 | 02 | 03 | 04 | 05 | 06 | 07 | 08 | 09 | 10 | 11 | 12 |
| FRI | 01 | 02 | 03 | 04 | 05 | 06 | 07 | 08 | 09 | 10 | 11 | 12 |
| SAT | 01 | 02 | 03 | 04 | 05 | 06 | 07 | 08 | 09 | 10 | 11 | 12 |
| SUN | 01 | 02 | 03 | 04 | 05 | 06 | 07 | 08 | 09 | 10 | 11 | 12 |
| MON | 01 | 02 | 03 | 04 | 05 | 06 | 07 | 08 | 09 | 10 | 11 | 12 |
| TUE | 01 | 02 | 03 | 04 | 05 | 06 | 07 | 08 | 09 | 10 | 11 | 12 |
| WED | 01 | 02 | 03 | 04 | 05 | 06 | 07 | 08 | 09 | 10 | 11 | 12 |
| THU | 01 | 02 | 03 | 04 | 05 | 06 | 07 | 08 | 09 | 10 | 11 | 12 |
| FRI | 01 | 02 | 03 | 04 | 05 | 06 | 07 | 08 | 09 | 10 | 11 | 12 |
| SAT | 01 | 02 | 03 | 04 | 05 | 06 | 07 | 08 | 09 | 10 | 11 | 12 |
| SUN | 01 | 02 | 03 | 04 | 05 | 06 | 07 | 08 | 09 | 10 | 11 | 12 |

**NOTES:**

**DATE I STARTED TRACKING:**

# DEPRESSION *Tracker*

Document the days when you experienced depression. This page includes a 3-week tracker.

DEPRESSION LEVELS (1-MILD, 10 SEVERE)

| | | | | | | | | | | | | |
|---|---|---|---|---|---|---|---|---|---|---|---|---|
| MON | 01 | 02 | 03 | 04 | 05 | 06 | 07 | 08 | 09 | 10 | 11 | 12 |
| TUE | 01 | 02 | 03 | 04 | 05 | 06 | 07 | 08 | 09 | 10 | 11 | 12 |
| WED | 01 | 02 | 03 | 04 | 05 | 06 | 07 | 08 | 09 | 10 | 11 | 12 |
| THU | 01 | 02 | 03 | 04 | 05 | 06 | 07 | 08 | 09 | 10 | 11 | 12 |
| FRI | 01 | 02 | 03 | 04 | 05 | 06 | 07 | 08 | 09 | 10 | 11 | 12 |
| SAT | 01 | 02 | 03 | 04 | 05 | 06 | 07 | 08 | 09 | 10 | 11 | 12 |
| SUN | 01 | 02 | 03 | 04 | 05 | 06 | 07 | 08 | 09 | 10 | 11 | 12 |
| MON | 01 | 02 | 03 | 04 | 05 | 06 | 07 | 08 | 09 | 10 | 11 | 12 |
| TUE | 01 | 02 | 03 | 04 | 05 | 06 | 07 | 08 | 09 | 10 | 11 | 12 |
| WED | 01 | 02 | 03 | 04 | 05 | 06 | 07 | 08 | 09 | 10 | 11 | 12 |
| THU | 01 | 02 | 03 | 04 | 05 | 06 | 07 | 08 | 09 | 10 | 11 | 12 |
| FRI | 01 | 02 | 03 | 04 | 05 | 06 | 07 | 08 | 09 | 10 | 11 | 12 |
| SAT | 01 | 02 | 03 | 04 | 05 | 06 | 07 | 08 | 09 | 10 | 11 | 12 |
| SUN | 01 | 02 | 03 | 04 | 05 | 06 | 07 | 08 | 09 | 10 | 11 | 12 |
| MON | 01 | 02 | 03 | 04 | 05 | 06 | 07 | 08 | 09 | 10 | 11 | 12 |
| TUE | 01 | 02 | 03 | 04 | 05 | 06 | 07 | 08 | 09 | 10 | 11 | 12 |
| WED | 01 | 02 | 03 | 04 | 05 | 06 | 07 | 08 | 09 | 10 | 11 | 12 |
| THU | 01 | 02 | 03 | 04 | 05 | 06 | 07 | 08 | 09 | 10 | 11 | 12 |
| FRI | 01 | 02 | 03 | 04 | 05 | 06 | 07 | 08 | 09 | 10 | 11 | 12 |
| SAT | 01 | 02 | 03 | 04 | 05 | 06 | 07 | 08 | 09 | 10 | 11 | 12 |
| SUN | 01 | 02 | 03 | 04 | 05 | 06 | 07 | 08 | 09 | 10 | 11 | 12 |

**NOTES:**

**DATE I STARTED TRACKING:**

# RESET *your mind*

We can't always control the way our thoughts but we can learn to transform negative feelings into positive ones and control our reactions and impulses. Use the chart below to start the process.

WHEN I FEEL LIKE:                    I WILL TRY TO CONTROL BY REACTIONS BY:

NOTES & REFLECTIONS                    DOODLES & SCRIBBLES

# LOVE *Yourself*

## STEP 1:  MAKE YOURSELF A PRIORITY

It's important to always put yourself first by listening to your inner voice. Let it guide you in eliminating toxic people and negative sources.  Don't be afraid to distance yourself from people and places that make you feel unhappy or who don't support your journey.

## STEP 2:  FACE YOUR FEARS

Don't be afraid to confront your fears and self-doubt. Why do you feel unworthy at times?  What are you most worried about?

## STEP 3:  BE ACCOUNTABLE

Hold yourself accountable for the things you can control and change.  There are things in your life only you can change.

## STEP 4:  FORGIVE YOURSELF

Let go of past mistakes – you can't go back in time. We all have regrets and while it's important to hold yourself accountable for mistakes, you can only truly heal when you learn to forgive yourself. Free your mind so it can focus on a better you and a happier tomorrow.

## STEP 5:  ACCEPT WHERE YOU ARE IN YOUR JOURNEY

Don't allow yourself to grow frustrated that you aren't able to race towards the finish line. Your journey will take time so give yourself permission to fail while also learning to accept where you are right now.  Take it one day at a time. You owe it to yourself to stay focused on the road ahead while celebrating every milestone along the way.

**Write down your thoughts, reflections and ideas below:**

*Thoughts*

# SELF CARE *Focus*

### TOP 3 SELF-CARE ACTIVITIES

### HOW THEY MAKE ME FEEL

1

2

3

## OTHER SELF-CARE ACTIVITIES THAT MAKE ME HAPPY

01

02

03

## FAVORITE QUOTES/WORDS OF ENCOURAGEMENT

# TRIGGER *Sources*

Discover what causes emotional pain and negative thoughts in your life.

## Describe the negative reaction/response you would like to overcome:

Consider the aspects of your life below and write down how each category can cause the above trigger.

### PERSONAL

### PEOPLE

### PLACES

### SITUATIONS

Think about the different ways you can overcome your triggers when dealing with each category.
How can you better control your reactions and manage frustrating situations?

# HAPPINESS *Tracker*

Keep track of how often you feel happy and calm and what you did to minimize negative responses.

DATE:

HAPPINESS RATING: ☆☆☆☆☆

DATE:

HAPPINESS RATING: ☆☆☆☆☆

DATE:

HAPPINESS RATING: ☆☆☆☆☆

DATE:

HAPPINESS RATING: ☆☆☆☆☆

DATE:

HAPPINESS RATING: ☆☆☆☆☆

DATE:

HAPPINESS RATING: ☆☆☆☆☆

# DAILY *Reflection*

**HOW I FEEL TODAY**

**MY GREATEST CHALLENGE**

**MOOD TRACKER:**

**MORNING:**

**EVENING:**

**I FELT HAPPY WHEN:**

**I FELT EXCITED WHEN:**

**I FELT ENERGIZED WHEN:**

## Today's Highlights

## What I'm Grateful For Today

# DAILY *Awareness*

MONTH:

| M | T | W | T | F | S | S |
|---|---|---|---|---|---|---|
| ☐ | ☐ | ☐ | ☐ | ☐ | ☐ | ☐ |

## HOW I'M FEELING TODAY

## 3 WORDS TO DESCRIBE MY DAY

## STRUGGLES

## HIGHLIGHT OF MY DAY

## DAILY ACCOMPLISHMENTS

DATE:

# DAILY *Reflection*

## HOW I FEEL TODAY

## MY GREATEST CHALLENGE

## MOOD TRACKER:

MORNING:

EVENING:

## I FELT HAPPY WHEN:

## I FELT EXCITED WHEN:

## I FELT ENERGIZED WHEN:

### Today's Highlights

### What I'm Grateful For Today

# DAILY *Awareness*

MONTH:

| M | T | W | T | F | S | S |
|---|---|---|---|---|---|---|
| ☐ | ☐ | ☐ | ☐ | ☐ | ☐ | ☐ |

## HOW I'M FEELING TODAY

## 3 WORDS TO DESCRIBE MY DAY

## STRUGGLES

## HIGHLIGHT OF MY DAY

## DAILY ACCOMPLISHMENTS

DATE:

# DAILY *Reflection*

**HOW I FEEL TODAY**

**MY GREATEST CHALLENGE**

**MOOD TRACKER:**

MORNING:

EVENING:

**I FELT HAPPY WHEN:**

**I FELT EXCITED WHEN:**

**I FELT ENERGIZED WHEN:**

*Today's Highlights*

*What I'm Grateful For Today*

# DAILY *Awareness*

MONTH:

| M | T | W | T | F | S | S |
|---|---|---|---|---|---|---|
| ☐ | ☐ | ☐ | ☐ | ☐ | ☐ | ☐ |

## HOW I'M FEELING TODAY

## 3 WORDS TO DESCRIBE MY DAY

## STRUGGLES

## HIGHLIGHT OF MY DAY

## DAILY ACCOMPLISHMENTS

DATE:

# DAILY *Reflection*

**HOW I FEEL TODAY**

**MY GREATEST CHALLENGE**

**MOOD TRACKER:**

MORNING:

EVENING:

**I FELT HAPPY WHEN:**

**I FELT EXCITED WHEN:**

**I FELT ENERGIZED WHEN:**

*Today's Highlights*

*What I'm Grateful For Today*

# DAILY *Awareness*

MONTH:

M T W T F S S

☐ ☐ ☐ ☐ ☐ ☐ ☐

## HOW I'M FEELING TODAY

## 3 WORDS TO DESCRIBE MY DAY

## STRUGGLES

## HIGHLIGHT OF MY DAY

## DAILY ACCOMPLISHMENTS

# DAILY Reflection

DATE:

**HOW I FEEL TODAY**

**MY GREATEST CHALLENGE**

**MOOD TRACKER:**

MORNING:

EVENING:

I FELT HAPPY WHEN:

I FELT EXCITED WHEN:

I FELT ENERGIZED WHEN:

## Today's Highlights

## What I'm Grateful For Today

# DAILY *Awareness*

MONTH:

| M | T | W | T | F | S | S |
|---|---|---|---|---|---|---|
| ☐ | ☐ | ☐ | ☐ | ☐ | ☐ | ☐ |

## HOW I'M FEELING TODAY

## 3 WORDS TO DESCRIBE MY DAY

## STRUGGLES

## HIGHLIGHT OF MY DAY

## DAILY ACCOMPLISHMENTS

DATE:

# DAILY *Reflection*

**HOW I FEEL TODAY**

**MY GREATEST CHALLENGE**

**MOOD TRACKER:**

MORNING:

EVENING:

**I FELT HAPPY WHEN:**

**I FELT EXCITED WHEN:**

**I FELT ENERGIZED WHEN:**

*Today's Highlights*

*What I'm Grateful For Today*

# DAILY Awareness

MONTH: _____

| M | T | W | T | F | S | S |
|---|---|---|---|---|---|---|
| ☐ | ☐ | ☐ | ☐ | ☐ | ☐ | ☐ |

## HOW I'M FEELING TODAY

## 3 WORDS TO DESCRIBE MY DAY

## STRUGGLES

## HIGHLIGHT OF MY DAY

## DAILY ACCOMPLISHMENTS

DATE:

# DAILY *Reflection*

**HOW I FEEL TODAY**

**MY GREATEST CHALLENGE**

**MOOD TRACKER:**

MORNING:

EVENING:

**I FELT HAPPY WHEN:**

**I FELT EXCITED WHEN:**

**I FELT ENERGIZED WHEN:**

*Today's Highlights*

*What I'm Grateful For Today*

# DAILY *Awareness*

MONTH:

| M | T | W | T | F | S | S |
|---|---|---|---|---|---|---|
| ☐ | ☐ | ☐ | ☐ | ☐ | ☐ | ☐ |

## HOW I'M FEELING TODAY

## 3 WORDS TO DESCRIBE MY DAY

## STRUGGLES

## HIGHLIGHT OF MY DAY

## DAILY ACCOMPLISHMENTS

# POST *Therapy Chart*

DATE:

## SUMMARY/OVERVIEW OF THERAPY SESSION

## WHAT WE DISCUSSED

## HOW IT MADE ME FEEL

## WHAT I LEARNED

## WHAT I WANT TO DISCUSS NEXT

**Rate your session to keep track of progress.**

SESSION SCORE

# WEEKLY *Assessment*

|  | SLEEP | MOOD | POSITIVES | NEGATIVES |
|---|---|---|---|---|
| MONDAY |  |  |  |  |
| TUESDAY |  |  |  |  |
| WEDNESDAY |  |  |  |  |
| THURSDAY |  |  |  |  |
| FRIDAY |  |  |  |  |
| SATURADAY |  |  |  |  |
| SUNDAY |  |  |  |  |

# WEEKLY *Reflections*

**Monday**

**Tuesday**

**Wednesday**

**Thursday**

**Friday**

**Saturday**

**Sunday**

# DAILY *Reflection*

**HOW I FEEL TODAY**

**MY GREATEST CHALLENGE**

**MOOD TRACKER:**

MORNING:

EVENING:

**I FELT HAPPY WHEN:**

**I FELT EXCITED WHEN:**

**I FELT ENERGIZED WHEN:**

*Today's Highlights*

*What I'm Grateful For Today*

# DAILY *Awareness*

MONTH:

| M | T | W | T | F | S | S |
|---|---|---|---|---|---|---|
| ☐ | ☐ | ☐ | ☐ | ☐ | ☐ | ☐ |

## HOW I'M FEELING TODAY

## 3 WORDS TO DESCRIBE MY DAY

## STRUGGLES

## HIGHLIGHT OF MY DAY

## DAILY ACCOMPLISHMENTS

# DAILY *Reflection*

**HOW I FEEL TODAY**

**MY GREATEST CHALLENGE**

**MOOD TRACKER:**

MORNING:

EVENING:

**I FELT HAPPY WHEN:**

**I FELT EXCITED WHEN:**

**I FELT ENERGIZED WHEN:**

*Today's Highlights*

*What I'm Grateful For Today*

# DAILY *Awareness*

MONTH: _____

| M | T | W | T | F | S | S |
|---|---|---|---|---|---|---|
| ☐ | ☐ | ☐ | ☐ | ☐ | ☐ | ☐ |

## HOW I'M FEELING TODAY

## 3 WORDS TO DESCRIBE MY DAY

## STRUGGLES

## HIGHLIGHT OF MY DAY

## DAILY ACCOMPLISHMENTS

# DAILY *Reflection*

**HOW I FEEL TODAY**

**MY GREATEST CHALLENGE**

**MOOD TRACKER:**

**MORNING:**

**EVENING:**

**I FELT HAPPY WHEN:**

**I FELT EXCITED WHEN:**

**I FELT ENERGIZED WHEN:**

## Today's Highlights

## What I'm Grateful For Today

# DAILY *Awareness*

MONTH:

| M | T | W | T | F | S | S |
|---|---|---|---|---|---|---|
| ☐ | ☐ | ☐ | ☐ | ☐ | ☐ | ☐ |

## HOW I'M FEELING TODAY

## 3 WORDS TO DESCRIBE MY DAY

## STRUGGLES

## HIGHLIGHT OF MY DAY

## DAILY ACCOMPLISHMENTS

DATE:

# DAILY *Reflection*

**HOW I FEEL TODAY**

**MY GREATEST CHALLENGE**

**MOOD TRACKER:**

MORNING:

EVENING:

**I FELT HAPPY WHEN:**

**I FELT EXCITED WHEN:**

**I FELT ENERGIZED WHEN:**

*Today's Highlights*

*What I'm Grateful For Today*

# DAILY *Awareness*

MONTH:

| M | T | W | T | F | S | S |
|---|---|---|---|---|---|---|
| ☐ | ☐ | ☐ | ☐ | ☐ | ☐ | ☐ |

## HOW I'M FEELING TODAY

## 3 WORDS TO DESCRIBE MY DAY

## STRUGGLES

## HIGHLIGHT OF MY DAY

## DAILY ACCOMPLISHMENTS

# DAILY *Reflection*

DATE:

**HOW I FEEL TODAY**

**MY GREATEST CHALLENGE**

**MOOD TRACKER:**

MORNING:

EVENING:

**I FELT HAPPY WHEN:**

**I FELT EXCITED WHEN:**

**I FELT ENERGIZED WHEN:**

*Today's Highlights*

*What I'm Grateful For Today*

# DAILY *Awareness*

MONTH:

| M | T | W | T | F | S | S |
|---|---|---|---|---|---|---|
| ☐ | ☐ | ☐ | ☐ | ☐ | ☐ | ☐ |

## HOW I'M FEELING TODAY

## 3 WORDS TO DESCRIBE MY DAY

## STRUGGLES

## HIGHLIGHT OF MY DAY

## DAILY ACCOMPLISHMENTS

DATE:

# DAILY *Reflection*

**HOW I FEEL TODAY**

**MY GREATEST CHALLENGE**

**MOOD TRACKER:**

MORNING:

EVENING:

**I FELT HAPPY WHEN:**

**I FELT EXCITED WHEN:**

**I FELT ENERGIZED WHEN:**

*Today's Highlights*

*What I'm Grateful For Today*

# DAILY *Awareness*

MONTH:

| M | T | W | T | F | S | S |
|---|---|---|---|---|---|---|
| ☐ | ☐ | ☐ | ☐ | ☐ | ☐ | ☐ |

## HOW I'M FEELING TODAY

## 3 WORDS TO DESCRIBE MY DAY

## STRUGGLES

## HIGHLIGHT OF MY DAY

## DAILY ACCOMPLISHMENTS

DATE:

# DAILY *Reflection*

**HOW I FEEL TODAY**

**MY GREATEST CHALLENGE**

**MOOD TRACKER:**

MORNING:

EVENING:

**I FELT HAPPY WHEN:**

**I FELT EXCITED WHEN:**

**I FELT ENERGIZED WHEN:**

*Today's Highlights*

*What I'm Grateful For Today*

# DAILY *Awareness*

MONTH: _____

| M | T | W | T | F | S | S |
|---|---|---|---|---|---|---|
| ☐ | ☐ | ☐ | ☐ | ☐ | ☐ | ☐ |

## HOW I'M FEELING TODAY

## 3 WORDS TO DESCRIBE MY DAY

## STRUGGLES

## HIGHLIGHT OF MY DAY

## DAILY ACCOMPLISHMENTS

# POST *Therapy Chart*

DATE:

## SUMMARY/OVERVIEW OF THERAPY SESSION

## WHAT WE DISCUSSED

## HOW IT MADE ME FEEL

## WHAT I LEARNED

## WHAT I WANT TO DISCUSS NEXT

**Rate your session to keep track of progress.**

SESSION SCORE

# WEEKLY *Assessment*

| | SLEEP | MOOD | POSITIVES | NEGATIVES |
|---|---|---|---|---|
| MONDAY | | | | |
| TUESDAY | | | | |
| WEDNESDAY | | | | |
| THURSDAY | | | | |
| FRIDAY | | | | |
| SATURADY | | | | |
| SUNDAY | | | | |

# WEEKLY *Reflections*

**Monday**

**Tuesday**

**Wednesday**

**Thursday**

**Friday**

**Saturday**

**Sunday**

DATE:

# DAILY *Reflection*

**HOW I FEEL TODAY**

**MY GREATEST CHALLENGE**

**MOOD TRACKER:**

**MORNING:**

**EVENING:**

**I FELT HAPPY WHEN:**

**I FELT EXCITED WHEN:**

**I FELT ENERGIZED WHEN:**

*Today's Highlights*

*What I'm Grateful For Today*

# DAILY *Awareness*

MONTH:

| M | T | W | T | F | S | S |
|---|---|---|---|---|---|---|
| ☐ | ☐ | ☐ | ☐ | ☐ | ☐ | ☐ |

## HOW I'M FEELING TODAY

## 3 WORDS TO DESCRIBE MY DAY

## STRUGGLES

## HIGHLIGHT OF MY DAY

## DAILY ACCOMPLISHMENTS

DATE:

# DAILY *Reflection*

**HOW I FEEL TODAY**

**MY GREATEST CHALLENGE**

**MOOD TRACKER:**

MORNING:

EVENING:

**I FELT HAPPY WHEN:**

**I FELT EXCITED WHEN:**

**I FELT ENERGIZED WHEN:**

*Today's Highlights*

*What I'm Grateful For Today*

# DAILY *Awareness*

MONTH:

| M | T | W | T | F | S | S |
|---|---|---|---|---|---|---|
| ☐ | ☐ | ☐ | ☐ | ☐ | ☐ | ☐ |

## HOW I'M FEELING TODAY

## 3 WORDS TO DESCRIBE MY DAY

## STRUGGLES

## HIGHLIGHT OF MY DAY

## DAILY ACCOMPLISHMENTS

# DAILY *Reflection*

DATE:

**HOW I FEEL TODAY**

**MY GREATEST CHALLENGE**

**MOOD TRACKER:**

**MORNING:**

**EVENING:**

**I FELT HAPPY WHEN:**

**I FELT EXCITED WHEN:**

**I FELT ENERGIZED WHEN:**

*Today's Highlights*

*What I'm Grateful For Today*

# DAILY *Awareness*

MONTH:

| M | T | W | T | F | S | S |
|---|---|---|---|---|---|---|
| ☐ | ☐ | ☐ | ☐ | ☐ | ☐ | ☐ |

## HOW I'M FEELING TODAY

## 3 WORDS TO DESCRIBE MY DAY

## STRUGGLES

## HIGHLIGHT OF MY DAY

## DAILY ACCOMPLISHMENTS

# DAILY *Reflection*

DATE:

**HOW I FEEL TODAY**

**MY GREATEST CHALLENGE**

**MOOD TRACKER:**

MORNING:

EVENING:

**I FELT HAPPY WHEN:**

**I FELT EXCITED WHEN:**

**I FELT ENERGIZED WHEN:**

*Today's Highlights*

*What I'm Grateful For Today*

# DAILY *Awareness*

MONTH:

| M | T | W | T | F | S | S |
|---|---|---|---|---|---|---|
| ☐ | ☐ | ☐ | ☐ | ☐ | ☐ | ☐ |

## HOW I'M FEELING TODAY

## 3 WORDS TO DESCRIBE MY DAY

## STRUGGLES

## HIGHLIGHT OF MY DAY

## DAILY ACCOMPLISHMENTS

# DAILY *Reflection*

DATE:

**HOW I FEEL TODAY**

**MY GREATEST CHALLENGE**

**MOOD TRACKER:**

**MORNING:**

**EVENING:**

**I FELT HAPPY WHEN:**

**I FELT EXCITED WHEN:**

**I FELT ENERGIZED WHEN:**

*Today's Highlights*

*What I'm Grateful For Today*

# DAILY *Awareness*

M  T  W  T  F  S  S
☐  ☐  ☐  ☐  ☐  ☐  ☐

## HOW I'M FEELING TODAY

## 3 WORDS TO DESCRIBE MY DAY

## STRUGGLES

## HIGHLIGHT OF MY DAY

## DAILY ACCOMPLISHMENTS

DATE:

# DAILY *Reflection*

**HOW I FEEL TODAY**

**MY GREATEST CHALLENGE**

**MOOD TRACKER:**

MORNING:

EVENING:

**I FELT HAPPY WHEN:**

**I FELT EXCITED WHEN:**

**I FELT ENERGIZED WHEN:**

*Today's Highlights*

*What I'm Grateful For Today*

# DAILY *Awareness*

MONTH:

| M | T | W | T | F | S | S |
|---|---|---|---|---|---|---|
| ☐ | ☐ | ☐ | ☐ | ☐ | ☐ | ☐ |

## HOW I'M FEELING TODAY

## 3 WORDS TO DESCRIBE MY DAY

## STRUGGLES

## HIGHLIGHT OF MY DAY

## DAILY ACCOMPLISHMENTS

# DAILY *Reflection*

**HOW I FEEL TODAY**

**MY GREATEST CHALLENGE**

**MOOD TRACKER:**

MORNING:

EVENING:

**I FELT HAPPY WHEN:**

**I FELT EXCITED WHEN:**

**I FELT ENERGIZED WHEN:**

*Today's Highlights*

*What I'm Grateful For Today*

# ANXIETY *Tracker*

Document the days when you experienced anxiety. This page includes a 3-week tracker.

ANXIETY LEVELS (1-MILD, 10 SEVERE)

| | | | | | | | | | | | | |
|---|---|---|---|---|---|---|---|---|---|---|---|---|
| MON | 01 | 02 | 03 | 04 | 05 | 06 | 07 | 08 | 09 | 10 | 11 | 12 |
| TUE | 01 | 02 | 03 | 04 | 05 | 06 | 07 | 08 | 09 | 10 | 11 | 12 |
| WED | 01 | 02 | 03 | 04 | 05 | 06 | 07 | 08 | 09 | 10 | 11 | 12 |
| THU | 01 | 02 | 03 | 04 | 05 | 06 | 07 | 08 | 09 | 10 | 11 | 12 |
| FRI | 01 | 02 | 03 | 04 | 05 | 06 | 07 | 08 | 09 | 10 | 11 | 12 |
| SAT | 01 | 02 | 03 | 04 | 05 | 06 | 07 | 08 | 09 | 10 | 11 | 12 |
| SUN | 01 | 02 | 03 | 04 | 05 | 06 | 07 | 08 | 09 | 10 | 11 | 12 |
| MON | 01 | 02 | 03 | 04 | 05 | 06 | 07 | 08 | 09 | 10 | 11 | 12 |
| TUE | 01 | 02 | 03 | 04 | 05 | 06 | 07 | 08 | 09 | 10 | 11 | 12 |
| WED | 01 | 02 | 03 | 04 | 05 | 06 | 07 | 08 | 09 | 10 | 11 | 12 |
| THU | 01 | 02 | 03 | 04 | 05 | 06 | 07 | 08 | 09 | 10 | 11 | 12 |
| FRI | 01 | 02 | 03 | 04 | 05 | 06 | 07 | 08 | 09 | 10 | 11 | 12 |
| SAT | 01 | 02 | 03 | 04 | 05 | 06 | 07 | 08 | 09 | 10 | 11 | 12 |
| SUN | 01 | 02 | 03 | 04 | 05 | 06 | 07 | 08 | 09 | 10 | 11 | 12 |
| MON | 01 | 02 | 03 | 04 | 05 | 06 | 07 | 08 | 09 | 10 | 11 | 12 |
| TUE | 01 | 02 | 03 | 04 | 05 | 06 | 07 | 08 | 09 | 10 | 11 | 12 |
| WED | 01 | 02 | 03 | 04 | 05 | 06 | 07 | 08 | 09 | 10 | 11 | 12 |
| THU | 01 | 02 | 03 | 04 | 05 | 06 | 07 | 08 | 09 | 10 | 11 | 12 |
| FRI | 01 | 02 | 03 | 04 | 05 | 06 | 07 | 08 | 09 | 10 | 11 | 12 |
| SAT | 01 | 02 | 03 | 04 | 05 | 06 | 07 | 08 | 09 | 10 | 11 | 12 |
| SUN | 01 | 02 | 03 | 04 | 05 | 06 | 07 | 08 | 09 | 10 | 11 | 12 |

**NOTES:**

**DATE I STARTED TRACKING:**

# DEPRESSION *Tracker*

Document the days when you experienced depression. This page includes a 3-week tracker.

**DEPRESSION LEVELS (1-MILD, 10 SEVERE)**

| Day | | | | | | | | | | | | |
|-----|---|---|---|---|---|---|---|---|---|---|---|---|
| MON | 01 | 02 | 03 | 04 | 05 | 06 | 07 | 08 | 09 | 10 | 11 | 12 |
| TUE | 01 | 02 | 03 | 04 | 05 | 06 | 07 | 08 | 09 | 10 | 11 | 12 |
| WED | 01 | 02 | 03 | 04 | 05 | 06 | 07 | 08 | 09 | 10 | 11 | 12 |
| THU | 01 | 02 | 03 | 04 | 05 | 06 | 07 | 08 | 09 | 10 | 11 | 12 |
| FRI | 01 | 02 | 03 | 04 | 05 | 06 | 07 | 08 | 09 | 10 | 11 | 12 |
| SAT | 01 | 02 | 03 | 04 | 05 | 06 | 07 | 08 | 09 | 10 | 11 | 12 |
| SUN | 01 | 02 | 03 | 04 | 05 | 06 | 07 | 08 | 09 | 10 | 11 | 12 |
| MON | 01 | 02 | 03 | 04 | 05 | 06 | 07 | 08 | 09 | 10 | 11 | 12 |
| TUE | 01 | 02 | 03 | 04 | 05 | 06 | 07 | 08 | 09 | 10 | 11 | 12 |
| WED | 01 | 02 | 03 | 04 | 05 | 06 | 07 | 08 | 09 | 10 | 11 | 12 |
| THU | 01 | 02 | 03 | 04 | 05 | 06 | 07 | 08 | 09 | 10 | 11 | 12 |
| FRI | 01 | 02 | 03 | 04 | 05 | 06 | 07 | 08 | 09 | 10 | 11 | 12 |
| SAT | 01 | 02 | 03 | 04 | 05 | 06 | 07 | 08 | 09 | 10 | 11 | 12 |
| SUN | 01 | 02 | 03 | 04 | 05 | 06 | 07 | 08 | 09 | 10 | 11 | 12 |
| MON | 01 | 02 | 03 | 04 | 05 | 06 | 07 | 08 | 09 | 10 | 11 | 12 |
| TUE | 01 | 02 | 03 | 04 | 05 | 06 | 07 | 08 | 09 | 10 | 11 | 12 |
| WED | 01 | 02 | 03 | 04 | 05 | 06 | 07 | 08 | 09 | 10 | 11 | 12 |
| THU | 01 | 02 | 03 | 04 | 05 | 06 | 07 | 08 | 09 | 10 | 11 | 12 |
| FRI | 01 | 02 | 03 | 04 | 05 | 06 | 07 | 08 | 09 | 10 | 11 | 12 |
| SAT | 01 | 02 | 03 | 04 | 05 | 06 | 07 | 08 | 09 | 10 | 11 | 12 |
| SUN | 01 | 02 | 03 | 04 | 05 | 06 | 07 | 08 | 09 | 10 | 11 | 12 |

**NOTES:**

**DATE I STARTED TRACKING:**

# DAILY *Awareness*

MONTH:

| M | T | W | T | F | S | S |
|---|---|---|---|---|---|---|
| ☐ | ☐ | ☐ | ☐ | ☐ | ☐ | ☐ |

## HOW I'M FEELING TODAY

## 3 WORDS TO DESCRIBE MY DAY

## STRUGGLES

## HIGHLIGHT OF MY DAY

## DAILY ACCOMPLISHMENTS

# POST *Therapy Chart*

DATE:

## SUMMARY/OVERVIEW OF THERAPY SESSION

## WHAT WE DISCUSSED

## HOW IT MADE ME FEEL

## WHAT I LEARNED

## WHAT I WANT TO DISCUSS NEXT

Rate your session to
keep track of progress.

SESSION SCORE

# THOUGHTS *Tracker*

MONITORING YOUR THOUGHTS & FEELINGS

### MONDAY'S THOUGHTS

### TUESDAY'S THOUGHTS

### WEDNESDAY'S THOUGHTS

### THURSDAY'S THOUGHTS

### FRIDAY'S THOUGHTS

### SATURDAY'S THOUGHTS

### SUNDAY'S THOUGHTS

# WEEKLY *Assessment*

| | SLEEP | MOOD | POSITIVES | NEGATIVES |
|---|---|---|---|---|
| MONDAY | | | | |
| TUESDAY | | | | |
| WEDNESDAY | | | | |
| THURSDAY | | | | |
| FRIDAY | | | | |
| SATURADY | | | | |
| SUNDAY | | | | |

# WEEKLY *Reflections*

### Monday

### Tuesday

### Wednesday

### Thursday

### Friday

### Saturday

### Sunday

# DAILY Reflection

DATE:

## HOW I FEEL TODAY

## MY GREATEST CHALLENGE

## MOOD TRACKER:

MORNING:

EVENING:

I FELT HAPPY WHEN:

I FELT EXCITED WHEN:

I FELT ENERGIZED WHEN:

## Today's Highlights

## What I'm Grateful For Today

# DAILY *Awareness*

MONTH:

M | T | W | T | F | S | S
--- | --- | --- | --- | --- | --- | ---
☐ | ☐ | ☐ | ☐ | ☐ | ☐ | ☐

## HOW I'M FEELING TODAY

## 3 WORDS TO DESCRIBE MY DAY

## STRUGGLES

## HIGHLIGHT OF MY DAY

## DAILY ACCOMPLISHMENTS

DATE:

# DAILY *Reflection*

**HOW I FEEL TODAY**

**MY GREATEST CHALLENGE**

**MOOD TRACKER:**

MORNING:

EVENING:

**I FELT HAPPY WHEN:**

**I FELT EXCITED WHEN:**

**I FELT ENERGIZED WHEN:**

*Today's Highlights*

*What I'm Grateful For Today*

# DAILY *Awareness*

MONTH:

| M | T | W | T | F | S | S |
|---|---|---|---|---|---|---|
| ☐ | ☐ | ☐ | ☐ | ☐ | ☐ | ☐ |

## HOW I'M FEELING TODAY

## 3 WORDS TO DESCRIBE MY DAY

## STRUGGLES

## HIGHLIGHT OF MY DAY

## DAILY ACCOMPLISHMENTS

# DAILY Reflection

DATE:

**HOW I FEEL TODAY**

**MY GREATEST CHALLENGE**

**MOOD TRACKER:**

MORNING:

EVENING:

**I FELT HAPPY WHEN:**

**I FELT EXCITED WHEN:**

**I FELT ENERGIZED WHEN:**

## Today's Highlights

## What I'm Grateful For Today

# DAILY *Awareness*

MONTH:

M T W T F S S
☐ ☐ ☐ ☐ ☐ ☐ ☐

## HOW I'M FEELING TODAY

## 3 WORDS TO DESCRIBE MY DAY

## STRUGGLES

## HIGHLIGHT OF MY DAY

## DAILY ACCOMPLISHMENTS

# DAILY *Reflection*

**HOW I FEEL TODAY**

**MY GREATEST CHALLENGE**

**MOOD TRACKER:**

MORNING:

EVENING:

**I FELT HAPPY WHEN:**

**I FELT EXCITED WHEN:**

**I FELT ENERGIZED WHEN:**

*Today's Highlights*

*What I'm Grateful For Today*

# DAILY *Awareness*

MONTH:

| M | T | W | T | F | S | S |
|---|---|---|---|---|---|---|
| ☐ | ☐ | ☐ | ☐ | ☐ | ☐ | ☐ |

## HOW I'M FEELING TODAY

## 3 WORDS TO DESCRIBE MY DAY

## STRUGGLES

## HIGHLIGHT OF MY DAY

## DAILY ACCOMPLISHMENTS

# DAILY Reflection

DATE:

## HOW I FEEL TODAY

## MY GREATEST CHALLENGE

## MOOD TRACKER:

MORNING:

EVENING:

### I FELT HAPPY WHEN:

### I FELT EXCITED WHEN:

### I FELT ENERGIZED WHEN:

### Today's Highlights

### What I'm Grateful For Today

# DAILY *Awareness*

MONTH:

| M | T | W | T | F | S | S |
|---|---|---|---|---|---|---|
| ☐ | ☐ | ☐ | ☐ | ☐ | ☐ | ☐ |

## HOW I'M FEELING TODAY

## 3 WORDS TO DESCRIBE MY DAY

## STRUGGLES

## HIGHLIGHT OF MY DAY

## DAILY ACCOMPLISHMENTS

# DAILY Reflection

DATE:

**HOW I FEEL TODAY**

**MY GREATEST CHALLENGE**

**MOOD TRACKER:**

MORNING:

EVENING:

I FELT HAPPY WHEN:

I FELT EXCITED WHEN:

I FELT ENERGIZED WHEN:

*Today's Highlights*

*What I'm Grateful For Today*

# DAILY *Awareness*

MONTH:

| M | T | W | T | F | S | S |
|---|---|---|---|---|---|---|
| ☐ | ☐ | ☐ | ☐ | ☐ | ☐ | ☐ |

## HOW I'M FEELING TODAY

## 3 WORDS TO DESCRIBE MY DAY

## STRUGGLES

## HIGHLIGHT OF MY DAY

## DAILY ACCOMPLISHMENTS

# DAILY *Reflection*

**HOW I FEEL TODAY**

**MY GREATEST CHALLENGE**

**MOOD TRACKER:**

MORNING:

EVENING:

**I FELT HAPPY WHEN:**

**I FELT EXCITED WHEN:**

**I FELT ENERGIZED WHEN:**

*Today's Highlights*

*What I'm Grateful For Today*

# DAILY *Awareness*

MONTH:

| M | T | W | T | F | S | S |
|---|---|---|---|---|---|---|
| ☐ | ☐ | ☐ | ☐ | ☐ | ☐ | ☐ |

## HOW I'M FEELING TODAY

## 3 WORDS TO DESCRIBE MY DAY

## STRUGGLES

## HIGHLIGHT OF MY DAY

## DAILY ACCOMPLISHMENTS

# POST Therapy Chart

DATE:

## SUMMARY/OVERVIEW OF THERAPY SESSION

## WHAT WE DISCUSSED

## HOW IT MADE ME FEEL

## WHAT I LEARNED

## WHAT I WANT TO DISCUSS NEXT

**Rate your session to keep track of progress.**

SESSION SCORE

# THOUGHTS *Tracker*

MONITORING YOUR THOUGHTS & FEELINGS

MONDAY'S THOUGHTS

TUESDAY'S THOUGHTS

WEDNESDAY'S THOUGHTS

THURSDAY'S THOUGHTS

FRIDAY'S THOUGHTS

SATURDAY'S THOUGHTS

SUNDAY'S THOUGHTS

# WEEKLY *Assessment*

| | SLEEP | MOOD | POSITIVES | NEGATIVES |
|---|---|---|---|---|
| MONDAY | | | | |
| TUESDAY | | | | |
| WEDNESDAY | | | | |
| THURSDAY | | | | |
| FRIDAY | | | | |
| SATURADY | | | | |
| SUNDAY | | | | |

# WEEKLY *Reflections*

### Monday

### Tuesday

### Wednesday

### Thursday

### Friday

### Saturday

### Sunday

DATE:

# DAILY *Reflection*

**HOW I FEEL TODAY**

**MY GREATEST CHALLENGE**

**MOOD TRACKER:**

MORNING:

EVENING:

**I FELT HAPPY WHEN:**

**I FELT EXCITED WHEN:**

**I FELT ENERGIZED WHEN:**

*Today's Highlights*

*What I'm Grateful For Today*

# DAILY *Awareness*

MONTH:

| M | T | W | T | F | S | S |
|---|---|---|---|---|---|---|
| ☐ | ☐ | ☐ | ☐ | ☐ | ☐ | ☐ |

## HOW I'M FEELING TODAY

## 3 WORDS TO DESCRIBE MY DAY

## STRUGGLES

## HIGHLIGHT OF MY DAY

## DAILY ACCOMPLISHMENTS

# DAILY *Reflection*

**HOW I FEEL TODAY**

**MY GREATEST CHALLENGE**

**MOOD TRACKER:**

MORNING:

EVENING:

**I FELT HAPPY WHEN:**

**I FELT EXCITED WHEN:**

**I FELT ENERGIZED WHEN:**

*Today's Highlights*

*What I'm Grateful For Today*

# DAILY *Awareness*

MONTH:

M T W T F S S

## HOW I'M FEELING TODAY

## 3 WORDS TO DESCRIBE MY DAY

## STRUGGLES

## HIGHLIGHT OF MY DAY

## DAILY ACCOMPLISHMENTS

# DAILY *Reflection*

DATE:

**HOW I FEEL TODAY**

**MY GREATEST CHALLENGE**

**MOOD TRACKER:**

MORNING:

EVENING:

**I FELT HAPPY WHEN:**

**I FELT EXCITED WHEN:**

**I FELT ENERGIZED WHEN:**

*Today's Highlights*

*What I'm Grateful For Today*

# DAILY *Awareness*

MONTH:

| M | T | W | T | F | S | S |
|---|---|---|---|---|---|---|
| ☐ | ☐ | ☐ | ☐ | ☐ | ☐ | ☐ |

## HOW I'M FEELING TODAY

## 3 WORDS TO DESCRIBE MY DAY

## STRUGGLES

## HIGHLIGHT OF MY DAY

## DAILY ACCOMPLISHMENTS

# DAILY *Reflection*

**HOW I FEEL TODAY**

**MY GREATEST CHALLENGE**

**MOOD TRACKER:**

MORNING:

EVENING:

**I FELT HAPPY WHEN:**

**I FELT EXCITED WHEN:**

**I FELT ENERGIZED WHEN:**

*Today's Highlights*

*What I'm Grateful For Today*

# DAILY *Awareness*

MONTH:

M  T  W  T  F  S  S
☐  ☐  ☐  ☐  ☐  ☐  ☐

## HOW I'M FEELING TODAY

## 3 WORDS TO DESCRIBE MY DAY

## STRUGGLES

## HIGHLIGHT OF MY DAY

## DAILY ACCOMPLISHMENTS

# DAILY *Reflection*

DATE:

**HOW I FEEL TODAY**

**MY GREATEST CHALLENGE**

**MOOD TRACKER:**

MORNING:

EVENING:

**I FELT HAPPY WHEN:**

**I FELT EXCITED WHEN:**

**I FELT ENERGIZED WHEN:**

*Today's Highlights*

*What I'm Grateful For Today*

# DAILY *Awareness*

MONTH:

| M | T | W | T | F | S | S |
|---|---|---|---|---|---|---|
| ☐ | ☐ | ☐ | ☐ | ☐ | ☐ | ☐ |

## HOW I'M FEELING TODAY

## 3 WORDS TO DESCRIBE MY DAY

## STRUGGLES

## HIGHLIGHT OF MY DAY

## DAILY ACCOMPLISHMENTS

# DAILY *Reflection*

DATE:

**HOW I FEEL TODAY**

**MY GREATEST CHALLENGE**

**MOOD TRACKER:**

MORNING:

EVENING:

**I FELT HAPPY WHEN:**

**I FELT EXCITED WHEN:**

**I FELT ENERGIZED WHEN:**

*Today's Highlights*

*What I'm Grateful For Today*

# DAILY *Awareness*

MONTH:

M   T   W   T   F   S   S
☐   ☐   ☐   ☐   ☐   ☐   ☐

## HOW I'M FEELING TODAY

## 3 WORDS TO DESCRIBE MY DAY

## STRUGGLES

## HIGHLIGHT OF MY DAY

## DAILY ACCOMPLISHMENTS

# DAILY *Reflection*

**DATE:**

**HOW I FEEL TODAY**

**MY GREATEST CHALLENGE**

**MOOD TRACKER:**

MORNING:

EVENING:

**I FELT HAPPY WHEN:**

**I FELT EXCITED WHEN:**

**I FELT ENERGIZED WHEN:**

*Today's Highlights*

*What I'm Grateful For Today*

# DAILY *Awareness*

MONTH:

M   T   W   T   F   S   S

☐  ☐  ☐  ☐  ☐  ☐  ☐

## HOW I'M FEELING TODAY

## 3 WORDS TO DESCRIBE MY DAY

## STRUGGLES

## HIGHLIGHT OF MY DAY

## DAILY ACCOMPLISHMENTS

# POST *Therapy Chart*

DATE: _____

## SUMMARY/OVERVIEW OF THERAPY SESSION

| WHAT WE DISCUSSED | HOW IT MADE ME FEEL |
|---|---|
|  |  |

## WHAT I LEARNED

## WHAT I WANT TO DISCUSS NEXT

**Rate your session to keep track of progress.**

# THOUGHTS Tracker

MONITORING YOUR THOUGHTS & FEELINGS

### MONDAY'S THOUGHTS

### TUESDAY'S THOUGHTS

### WEDNESDAY'S THOUGHTS

### THURSDAY'S THOUGHTS

### FRIDAY'S THOUGHTS

### SATURDAY'S THOUGHTS

### SUNDAY'S THOUGHTS

# WEEKLY *Assessment*

| | SLEEP | MOOD | POSITIVES | NEGATIVES |
|---|---|---|---|---|
| MONDAY | | | | |
| TUESDAY | | | | |
| WEDNESDAY | | | | |
| THURSDAY | | | | |
| FRIDAY | | | | |
| SATURADY | | | | |
| SUNDAY | | | | |

# WEEKLY *Reflections*

**Monday**

**Tuesday**

**Wednesday**

**Thursday**

**Friday**

**Saturday**

**Sunday**

# DAILY *Reflection*

DATE:

## HOW I FEEL TODAY

## MY GREATEST CHALLENGE

## MOOD TRACKER:

MORNING:

EVENING:

I FELT HAPPY WHEN:

I FELT EXCITED WHEN:

I FELT ENERGIZED WHEN:

*Today's Highlights*

*What I'm Grateful For Today*

# DAILY *Awareness*

MONTH:

| M | T | W | T | F | S | S |
|---|---|---|---|---|---|---|
| ☐ | ☐ | ☐ | ☐ | ☐ | ☐ | ☐ |

## HOW I'M FEELING TODAY

## 3 WORDS TO DESCRIBE MY DAY

## STRUGGLES

## HIGHLIGHT OF MY DAY

## DAILY ACCOMPLISHMENTS

# DAILY *Reflection*

DATE:

**HOW I FEEL TODAY**

**MY GREATEST CHALLENGE**

**MOOD TRACKER:**

MORNING:

EVENING:

**I FELT HAPPY WHEN:**

**I FELT EXCITED WHEN:**

**I FELT ENERGIZED WHEN:**

*Today's Highlights*

*What I'm Grateful For Today*

# DAILY *Awareness*

MONTH:

| M | T | W | T | F | S | S |
|---|---|---|---|---|---|---|
| ☐ | ☐ | ☐ | ☐ | ☐ | ☐ | ☐ |

## HOW I'M FEELING TODAY

## 3 WORDS TO DESCRIBE MY DAY

## STRUGGLES

## HIGHLIGHT OF MY DAY

## DAILY ACCOMPLISHMENTS

# DAILY *Reflection*

**HOW I FEEL TODAY**

**MY GREATEST CHALLENGE**

**MOOD TRACKER:**

MORNING:

EVENING:

**I FELT HAPPY WHEN:**

**I FELT EXCITED WHEN:**

**I FELT ENERGIZED WHEN:**

*Today's Highlights*

*What I'm Grateful For Today*

# DAILY *Awareness*

MONTH: _____

| M | T | W | T | F | S | S |
|---|---|---|---|---|---|---|
| ☐ | ☐ | ☐ | ☐ | ☐ | ☐ | ☐ |

## HOW I'M FEELING TODAY

## 3 WORDS TO DESCRIBE MY DAY

## STRUGGLES

## HIGHLIGHT OF MY DAY

## DAILY ACCOMPLISHMENTS

# DAILY *Reflection*

**HOW I FEEL TODAY**

**MY GREATEST CHALLENGE**

**MOOD TRACKER:**

MORNING:

EVENING:

**I FELT HAPPY WHEN:**

**I FELT EXCITED WHEN:**

**I FELT ENERGIZED WHEN:**

*Today's Highlights*

*What I'm Grateful For Today*

# DAILY *Awareness*

MONTH:

M  T  W  T  F  S  S
☐  ☐  ☐  ☐  ☐  ☐  ☐

## HOW I'M FEELING TODAY

## 3 WORDS TO DESCRIBE MY DAY

## STRUGGLES

## HIGHLIGHT OF MY DAY

## DAILY ACCOMPLISHMENTS

# DAILY *Reflection*

**HOW I FEEL TODAY**

**MY GREATEST CHALLENGE**

**MOOD TRACKER:**

MORNING:

EVENING:

**I FELT HAPPY WHEN:**

**I FELT EXCITED WHEN:**

**I FELT ENERGIZED WHEN:**

*Today's Highlights*

*What I'm Grateful For Today*

# DAILY *Awareness*

MONTH:

| M | T | W | T | F | S | S |
|---|---|---|---|---|---|---|
| ☐ | ☐ | ☐ | ☐ | ☐ | ☐ | ☐ |

## HOW I'M FEELING TODAY

## 3 WORDS TO DESCRIBE MY DAY

## STRUGGLES

## HIGHLIGHT OF MY DAY

## DAILY ACCOMPLISHMENTS

# DAILY *Reflection*

DATE:

**HOW I FEEL TODAY**

**MY GREATEST CHALLENGE**

**MOOD TRACKER:**

MORNING:

EVENING:

I FELT HAPPY WHEN:

I FELT EXCITED WHEN:

I FELT ENERGIZED WHEN:

*Today's Highlights*

*What I'm Grateful For Today*

# DAILY *Awareness*

MONTH:

| M | T | W | T | F | S | S |
|---|---|---|---|---|---|---|
| ☐ | ☐ | ☐ | ☐ | ☐ | ☐ | ☐ |

## HOW I'M FEELING TODAY

## 3 WORDS TO DESCRIBE MY DAY

## STRUGGLES

## HIGHLIGHT OF MY DAY

## DAILY ACCOMPLISHMENTS

DATE:

# DAILY *Reflection*

**HOW I FEEL TODAY**

**MY GREATEST CHALLENGE**

**MOOD TRACKER:**

MORNING:

EVENING:

**I FELT HAPPY WHEN:**

**I FELT EXCITED WHEN:**

**I FELT ENERGIZED WHEN:**

*Today's Highlights*

*What I'm Grateful For Today*

# DAILY *Awareness*

MONTH:

| M | T | W | T | F | S | S |
|---|---|---|---|---|---|---|
| ☐ | ☐ | ☐ | ☐ | ☐ | ☐ | ☐ |

## HOW I'M FEELING TODAY

## 3 WORDS TO DESCRIBE MY DAY

## STRUGGLES

## HIGHLIGHT OF MY DAY

## DAILY ACCOMPLISHMENTS

# POST *Therapy Chart*

DATE:

## SUMMARY/OVERVIEW OF THERAPY SESSION

## WHAT WE DISCUSSED

## HOW IT MADE ME FEEL

## WHAT I LEARNED

## WHAT I WANT TO DISCUSS NEXT

Rate your session to keep track of progress.

SESSION SCORE

# THOUGHTS *Tracker*

MONITORING YOUR THOUGHTS & FEELINGS

MONDAY'S THOUGHTS

TUESDAY'S THOUGHTS

WEDNESDAY'S THOUGHTS

THURSDAY'S THOUGHTS

FRIDAY'S THOUGHTS

SATURDAY'S THOUGHTS

SUNDAY'S THOUGHTS

# WEEKLY *Reflections*

**Monday**

**Tuesday**

**Wednesday**

**Thursday**

**Friday**

**Saturday**

**Sunday**

# DAILY *Reflection*

**HOW I FEEL TODAY**

**MY GREATEST CHALLENGE**

**MOOD TRACKER:**

MORNING:

EVENING:

I FELT HAPPY WHEN:

I FELT EXCITED WHEN:

I FELT ENERGIZED WHEN:

*Today's Highlights*

*What I'm Grateful For Today*

# DAILY *Awareness*

MONTH:

| M | T | W | T | F | S | S |
|---|---|---|---|---|---|---|
| ☐ | ☐ | ☐ | ☐ | ☐ | ☐ | ☐ |

## HOW I'M FEELING TODAY

## 3 WORDS TO DESCRIBE MY DAY

## STRUGGLES

## HIGHLIGHT OF MY DAY

## DAILY ACCOMPLISHMENTS

# DAILY *Reflection*

**HOW I FEEL TODAY**

**MY GREATEST CHALLENGE**

**MOOD TRACKER:**

MORNING:

EVENING:

**I FELT HAPPY WHEN:**

**I FELT EXCITED WHEN:**

**I FELT ENERGIZED WHEN:**

*Today's Highlights*

*What I'm Grateful For Today*

# DAILY *Awareness*

MONTH: _____

| M | T | W | T | F | S | S |
|---|---|---|---|---|---|---|
| ☐ | ☐ | ☐ | ☐ | ☐ | ☐ | ☐ |

## HOW I'M FEELING TODAY

## 3 WORDS TO DESCRIBE MY DAY

## STRUGGLES

## HIGHLIGHT OF MY DAY

## DAILY ACCOMPLISHMENTS

DATE:

# DAILY *Reflection*

**HOW I FEEL TODAY**

**MY GREATEST CHALLENGE**

**MOOD TRACKER:**

MORNING:

EVENING:

**I FELT HAPPY WHEN:**

**I FELT EXCITED WHEN:**

**I FELT ENERGIZED WHEN:**

*Today's Highlights*

*What I'm Grateful For Today*

# DAILY *Awareness*

MONTH:

M T W T F S S
☐ ☐ ☐ ☐ ☐ ☐ ☐

## HOW I'M FEELING TODAY

## 3 WORDS TO DESCRIBE MY DAY

## STRUGGLES

## HIGHLIGHT OF MY DAY

## DAILY ACCOMPLISHMENTS

# DAILY *Reflection*

**HOW I FEEL TODAY**

**MY GREATEST CHALLENGE**

**MOOD TRACKER:**

**MORNING:**

**EVENING:**

**I FELT HAPPY WHEN:**

**I FELT EXCITED WHEN:**

**I FELT ENERGIZED WHEN:**

*Today's Highlights*

*What I'm Grateful For Today*

# DAILY *Awareness*

MONTH: _____

M T W T F S S
☐ ☐ ☐ ☐ ☐ ☐ ☐

## HOW I'M FEELING TODAY

## 3 WORDS TO DESCRIBE MY DAY

## STRUGGLES

## HIGHLIGHT OF MY DAY

## DAILY ACCOMPLISHMENTS

# DAILY *Reflection*

**HOW I FEEL TODAY**

**MY GREATEST CHALLENGE**

**MOOD TRACKER:**

MORNING:

EVENING:

**I FELT HAPPY WHEN:**

**I FELT EXCITED WHEN:**

**I FELT ENERGIZED WHEN:**

*Today's Highlights*

*What I'm Grateful For Today*

# DAILY *Awareness*

MONTH: _____

M ☐ T ☐ W ☐ T ☐ F ☐ S ☐ S ☐

## HOW I'M FEELING TODAY

## 3 WORDS TO DESCRIBE MY DAY

## STRUGGLES

## HIGHLIGHT OF MY DAY

## DAILY ACCOMPLISHMENTS

# DAILY *Reflection*

DATE:

**HOW I FEEL TODAY**

**MY GREATEST CHALLENGE**

**MOOD TRACKER:**

MORNING:

EVENING:

**I FELT HAPPY WHEN:**

**I FELT EXCITED WHEN:**

**I FELT ENERGIZED WHEN:**

*Today's Highlights*

*What I'm Grateful For Today*

# DAILY *Awareness*

MONTH:

| M | T | W | T | F | S | S |
|---|---|---|---|---|---|---|
| ☐ | ☐ | ☐ | ☐ | ☐ | ☐ | ☐ |

## HOW I'M FEELING TODAY

## 3 WORDS TO DESCRIBE MY DAY

## STRUGGLES

## HIGHLIGHT OF MY DAY

## DAILY ACCOMPLISHMENTS

# DAILY *Reflection*

**HOW I FEEL TODAY**

**MY GREATEST CHALLENGE**

**MOOD TRACKER:**

MORNING:

EVENING:

**I FELT HAPPY WHEN:**

**I FELT EXCITED WHEN:**

**I FELT ENERGIZED WHEN:**

## Today's Highlights

## What I'm Grateful For Today

# DAILY *Awareness*

MONTH:

| M | T | W | T | F | S | S |
|---|---|---|---|---|---|---|
| ☐ | ☐ | ☐ | ☐ | ☐ | ☐ | ☐ |

## HOW I'M FEELING TODAY

## 3 WORDS TO DESCRIBE MY DAY

## STRUGGLES

## HIGHLIGHT OF MY DAY

## DAILY ACCOMPLISHMENTS

# POST *Therapy Chart*

DATE:

## SUMMARY/OVERVIEW OF THERAPY SESSION

## WHAT WE DISCUSSED

## HOW IT MADE ME FEEL

## WHAT I LEARNED

## WHAT I WANT TO DISCUSS NEXT

Rate your session to keep track of progress.

SESSION SCORE

# THOUGHTS *Tracker*

MONITORING YOUR THOUGHTS & FEELINGS

MONDAY'S THOUGHTS

TUESDAY'S THOUGHTS

WEDNESDAY'S THOUGHTS

THURSDAY'S THOUGHTS

FRIDAY'S THOUGHTS

SATURDAY'S THOUGHTS

SUNDAY'S THOUGHTS

# WEEKLY *Reflections*

## Monday

## Tuesday

## Wednesday

## Thursday

## Friday

## Saturday

## Sunday

# DAILY *Reflection*

DATE:

**HOW I FEEL TODAY**

**MY GREATEST CHALLENGE**

**MOOD TRACKER:**

MORNING:

EVENING:

**I FELT HAPPY WHEN:**

**I FELT EXCITED WHEN:**

**I FELT ENERGIZED WHEN:**

*Today's Highlights*

*What I'm Grateful For Today*

# DAILY *Awareness*

MONTH:

| M | T | W | T | F | S | S |
|---|---|---|---|---|---|---|
| ☐ | ☐ | ☐ | ☐ | ☐ | ☐ | ☐ |

## HOW I'M FEELING TODAY

## 3 WORDS TO DESCRIBE MY DAY

## STRUGGLES

## HIGHLIGHT OF MY DAY

## DAILY ACCOMPLISHMENTS

# DAILY *Reflection*

DATE:

**HOW I FEEL TODAY**

**MY GREATEST CHALLENGE**

**MOOD TRACKER:**

MORNING:

EVENING:

**I FELT HAPPY WHEN:**

**I FELT EXCITED WHEN:**

**I FELT ENERGIZED WHEN:**

*Today's Highlights*

*What I'm Grateful For Today*

# DAILY *Awareness*

MONTH:

| M | T | W | T | F | S | S |
|---|---|---|---|---|---|---|
| ☐ | ☐ | ☐ | ☐ | ☐ | ☐ | ☐ |

## HOW I'M FEELING TODAY

## 3 WORDS TO DESCRIBE MY DAY

## STRUGGLES

## HIGHLIGHT OF MY DAY

## DAILY ACCOMPLISHMENTS

# DAILY *Reflection*

**HOW I FEEL TODAY**

**MY GREATEST CHALLENGE**

**MOOD TRACKER:**

MORNING:

EVENING:

**I FELT HAPPY WHEN:**

**I FELT EXCITED WHEN:**

**I FELT ENERGIZED WHEN:**

## Today's Highlights

## What I'm Grateful For Today

# DAILY *Awareness*

## HOW I'M FEELING TODAY

## 3 WORDS TO DESCRIBE MY DAY

## STRUGGLES

## HIGHLIGHT OF MY DAY

## DAILY ACCOMPLISHMENTS

# DAILY *Reflection*

**HOW I FEEL TODAY**

**MY GREATEST CHALLENGE**

**MOOD TRACKER:**

MORNING:

EVENING:

**I FELT HAPPY WHEN:**

**I FELT EXCITED WHEN:**

**I FELT ENERGIZED WHEN:**

*Today's Highlights*

*What I'm Grateful For Today*

# DAILY *Awareness*

MONTH:

| M | T | W | T | F | S | S |
|---|---|---|---|---|---|---|
| ☐ | ☐ | ☐ | ☐ | ☐ | ☐ | ☐ |

## HOW I'M FEELING TODAY

## 3 WORDS TO DESCRIBE MY DAY

## STRUGGLES

## HIGHLIGHT OF MY DAY

## DAILY ACCOMPLISHMENTS

# DAILY *Reflection*

**HOW I FEEL TODAY**

**MY GREATEST CHALLENGE**

**MOOD TRACKER:**

**MORNING:**

**EVENING:**

**I FELT HAPPY WHEN:**

**I FELT EXCITED WHEN:**

**I FELT ENERGIZED WHEN:**

*Today's Highlights*

*What I'm Grateful For Today*

# DAILY *Awareness*

MONTH:

M T W T F S S
☐ ☐ ☐ ☐ ☐ ☐ ☐

## HOW I'M FEELING TODAY

## 3 WORDS TO DESCRIBE MY DAY

## STRUGGLES

## HIGHLIGHT OF MY DAY

## DAILY ACCOMPLISHMENTS

# DAILY *Reflection*

**HOW I FEEL TODAY**

**MY GREATEST CHALLENGE**

**MOOD TRACKER:**

MORNING:

EVENING:

**I FELT HAPPY WHEN:**

**I FELT EXCITED WHEN:**

**I FELT ENERGIZED WHEN:**

*Today's Highlights*

*What I'm Grateful For Today*

# DAILY *Awareness*

MONTH:

| M | T | W | T | F | S | S |
|---|---|---|---|---|---|---|
| ☐ | ☐ | ☐ | ☐ | ☐ | ☐ | ☐ |

## HOW I'M FEELING TODAY

## 3 WORDS TO DESCRIBE MY DAY

## STRUGGLES

## HIGHLIGHT OF MY DAY

## DAILY ACCOMPLISHMENTS

# DAILY *Reflection*

**HOW I FEEL TODAY**

**MY GREATEST CHALLENGE**

**MOOD TRACKER:**

**MORNING:**

**EVENING:**

**I FELT HAPPY WHEN:**

**I FELT EXCITED WHEN:**

**I FELT ENERGIZED WHEN:**

*Today's Highlights*

*What I'm Grateful For Today*

# DAILY *Awareness*

MONTH:

M  T  W  T  F  S  S
☐  ☐  ☐  ☐  ☐  ☐  ☐

## HOW I'M FEELING TODAY

## 3 WORDS TO DESCRIBE MY DAY

## STRUGGLES

## HIGHLIGHT OF MY DAY

## DAILY ACCOMPLISHMENTS

# POST Therapy Chart

DATE:

## SUMMARY/OVERVIEW OF THERAPY SESSION

## WHAT WE DISCUSSED

## HOW IT MADE ME FEEL

## WHAT I LEARNED

## WHAT I WANT TO DISCUSS NEXT

**Rate your session to keep track of progress.**

SESSION SCORE

# THOUGHTS *Tracker*

MONITORING YOUR THOUGHTS & FEELINGS

MONDAY'S THOUGHTS

TUESDAY'S THOUGHTS

WEDNESDAY'S THOUGHTS

THURSDAY'S THOUGHTS

FRIDAY'S THOUGHTS

SATURDAY'S THOUGHTS

SUNDAY'S THOUGHTS

# WEEKLY *Reflections*

**Monday**

**Tuesday**

**Wednesday**

**Thursday**

**Friday**

**Saturday**

**Sunday**

Made in the USA
Monee, IL
09 July 2022